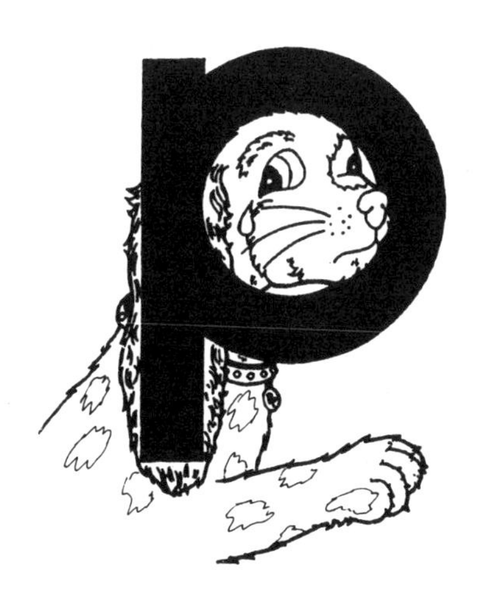

Hello. My name is **Poor Peter**.
Do you think I look hap

What makes you sad?

What makes you happ

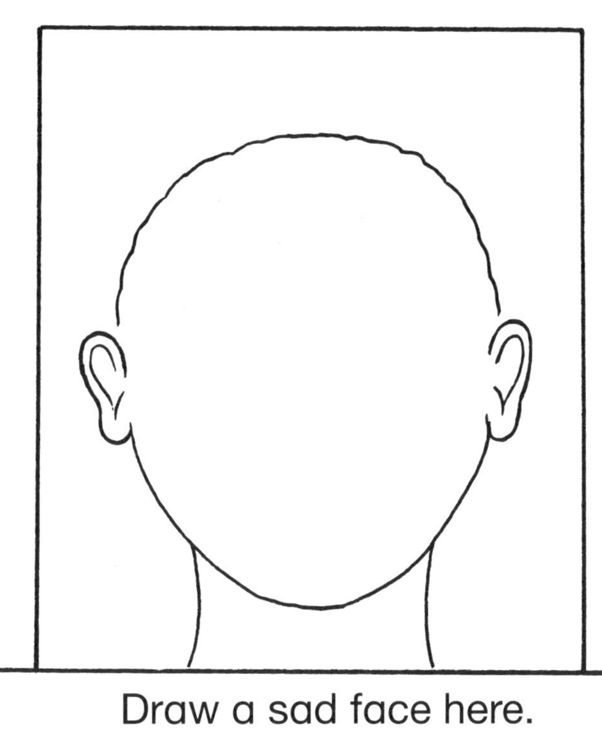

Draw a sad face here.

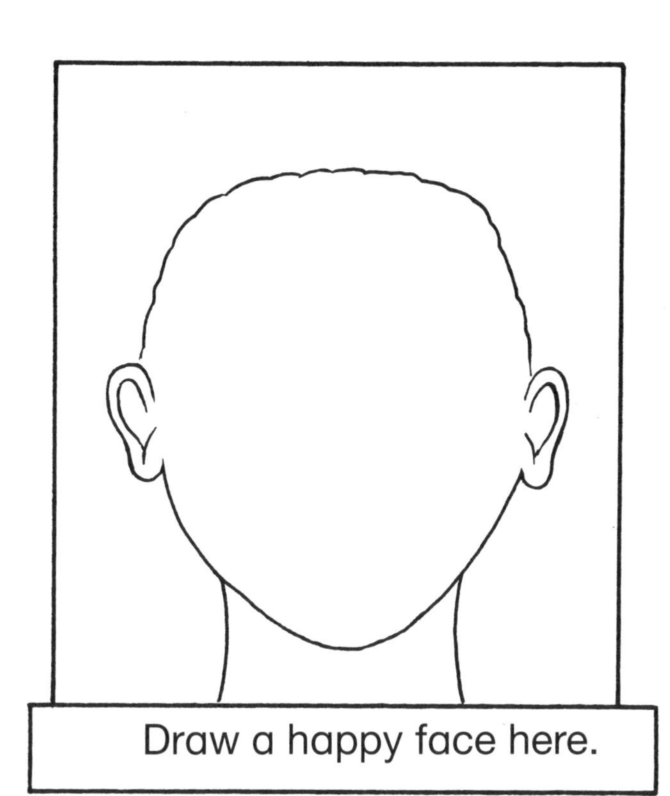

Draw a happy face here.

Can you remember these Letterland friends?

She looks quite cross! It's **Quarrelsome Queen**.

Here's the **Hairy Hat Man**. He looks very **h**appy.

Can you draw a handkerchief in my paw so I can wipe away my tear? Then I'll be happy too.

Let's meet some more of my Letterland friends.

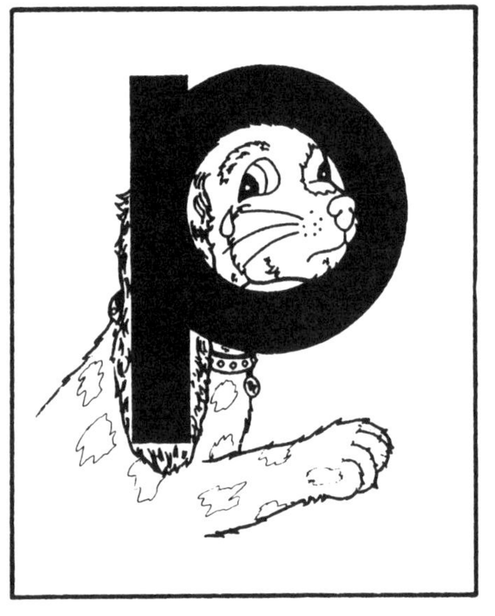

Here I am again! I am a Letterland **p**uppy so instead of barking, I just whisper this little sound at the start of my name. **P**oor **P**eter.

Point to my letter and whisper my sound each time.

p p p p

Colour me in.

Let's write my letter.
Stroke down my droopy ear.
Then go up and around my face.

Practise my letter and whisper my sound each time.

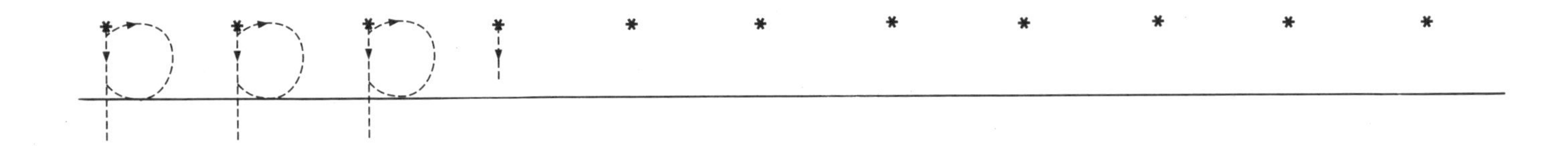

Colour in all the things that begin with **Poor Peter's** sound.

Hello! I am **Kicking King**. I make the sound at the start of my name. **K**icking **K**ing.

Point and whisper my sound each time.

k k k k

Colour me in.

Let's make my letter.
Start at my shoulder and go straight down to my foot. Add my arm and my **k**icking leg.

Whisper my sound as you write.

Kicking King is sharing his **k**ites with **Poor Peter** and **Ticking Tess**.

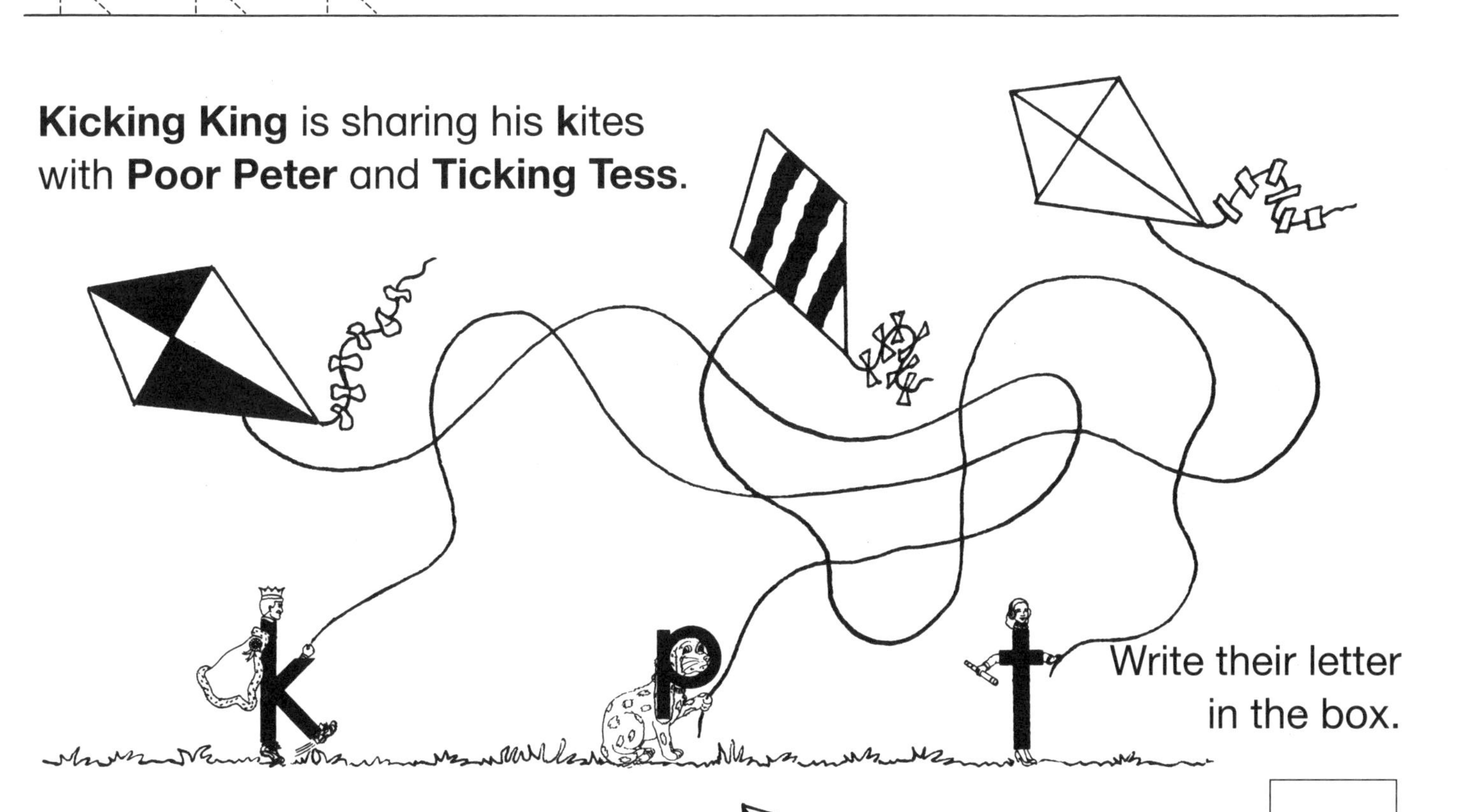

Write their letter in the box.

Who is flying this **k**ite? ___ ________________ [ ]

Who is flying this **k**ite? ___ ________________ [ ]

Who is flying this **k**ite? ___ ________________ [ ]

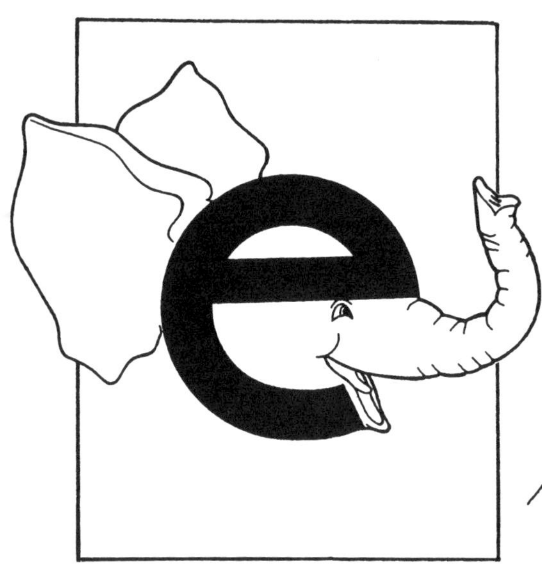

Hello **e**verybody! I'm **Eddy Elephant**. I know **e**verybody in Letterland – and **e**verybody knows me! I make the sound at the start of my name. **E**ddy **E**lephant.

Point and make my sound each time.

e e e e

Colour me in.

To write my letter start at my headband, go over my head and round my under my chin.

Make my sound as you write.

Elephants are very heavy.
Colour in all the heavy things in this picture.

Meet **Lamp Lady Lucy**. She shines her **l**ight all over Letterland. The **Lamp Lady** makes the gentle sound at the start of her name.
Lamp **L**ady **L**ucy.

Point and make her sound.

l l l l

Colour her in.

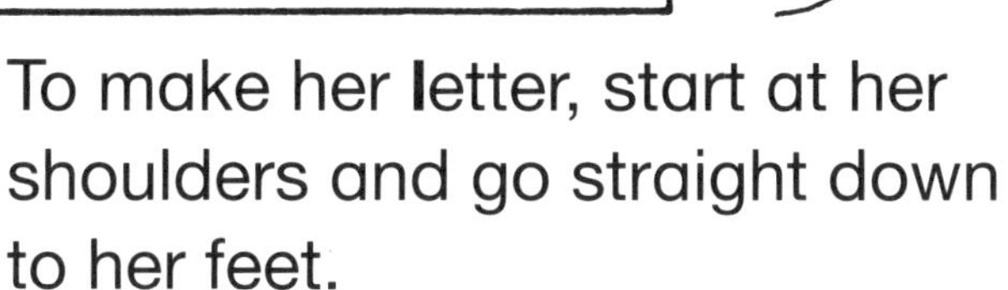

To make her **l**etter, start at her shoulders and go straight down to her feet.

Make her sound as you write.

Colour in the shapes in the picture where you see **Lamp Lady Lucy's l**etter.

What do you find?

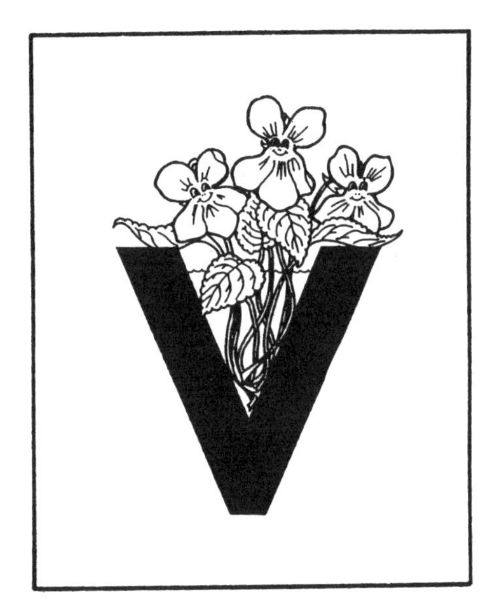

Here is **Vase of Violets**. **V**ery pleased to meet you! They make the soft sound at the start of **v**ase and **v**iolets. **V**ase of **V**iolets.

Point and whisper the sound each time.

Colour in the **v**ase and the **v**iolets.

To make the letter just start at the top of the **v**ase, go straight down and straight up the other side.

Whisper the sound as you write.

Vase of Violets' Flower Shop

Someone has forgotten to put the **v**ases on the shelves. Can you write some **Vase of Violet** letters to stand all the flowers in? Now colour them in!

Watch out! It's the **Wicked Water Witch**! Mind she doesn't **w**et you! She makes the sound at the start of her name. **W**icked **W**ater **W**itch.

Point and make her sound each time.

w w w w

Colour her in.

To write her letter just start at the top of her **w**ell, go down and up, and down and up again.

Make her sound as you practise.

It is **w**et and **w**indy in Letterland. **W**onderful **w**eather for the **Wicked Water Witch**! The **w**ind is **w**histling and **w**hirling her **w**indmill around. Even the **w**orms have come out to **w**iggle in the **w**et mud. Colour in only the things that begin with the **Wicked Water Witch's** sound.

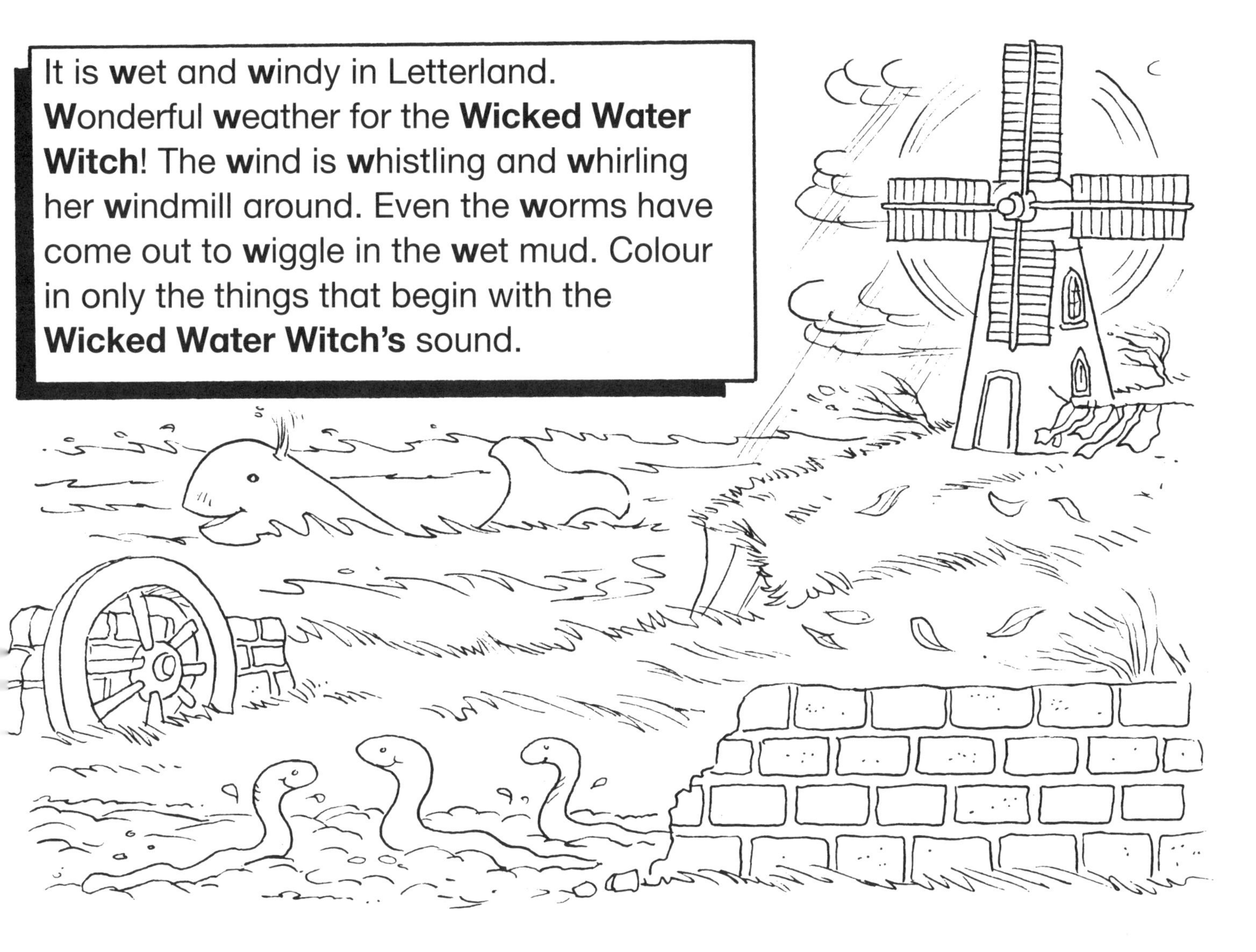

Jumping **J**ellybeans! It's **Jumping Jim**! He makes the sound at the start of his name. **J**umping **J**im.

Point and make his sound each time.

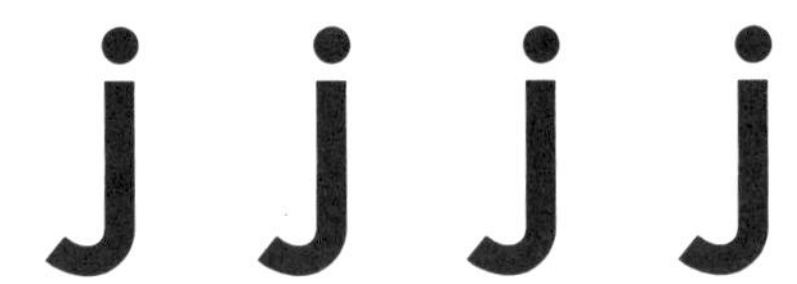

Colour him in.

To write his letter go down his body and around his knees to his feet. Don't forget his ball!

Make his sound as you write.

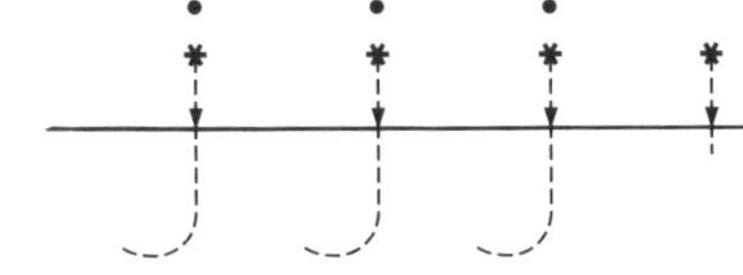

Jumping Jim is the best **j**umper in Letterland. Here are some more expert **j**umpers. Colour in each **j**umping animal and write **Jumping Jim's** letter in the box. What word have you helped to make?

_ump

_ump

_ump

_ump

_ump

The Letterland Circus is giving a show.
Colour in all your Letterland friends.
As you find each one, write their letter in a box.
k l v j r x z t h

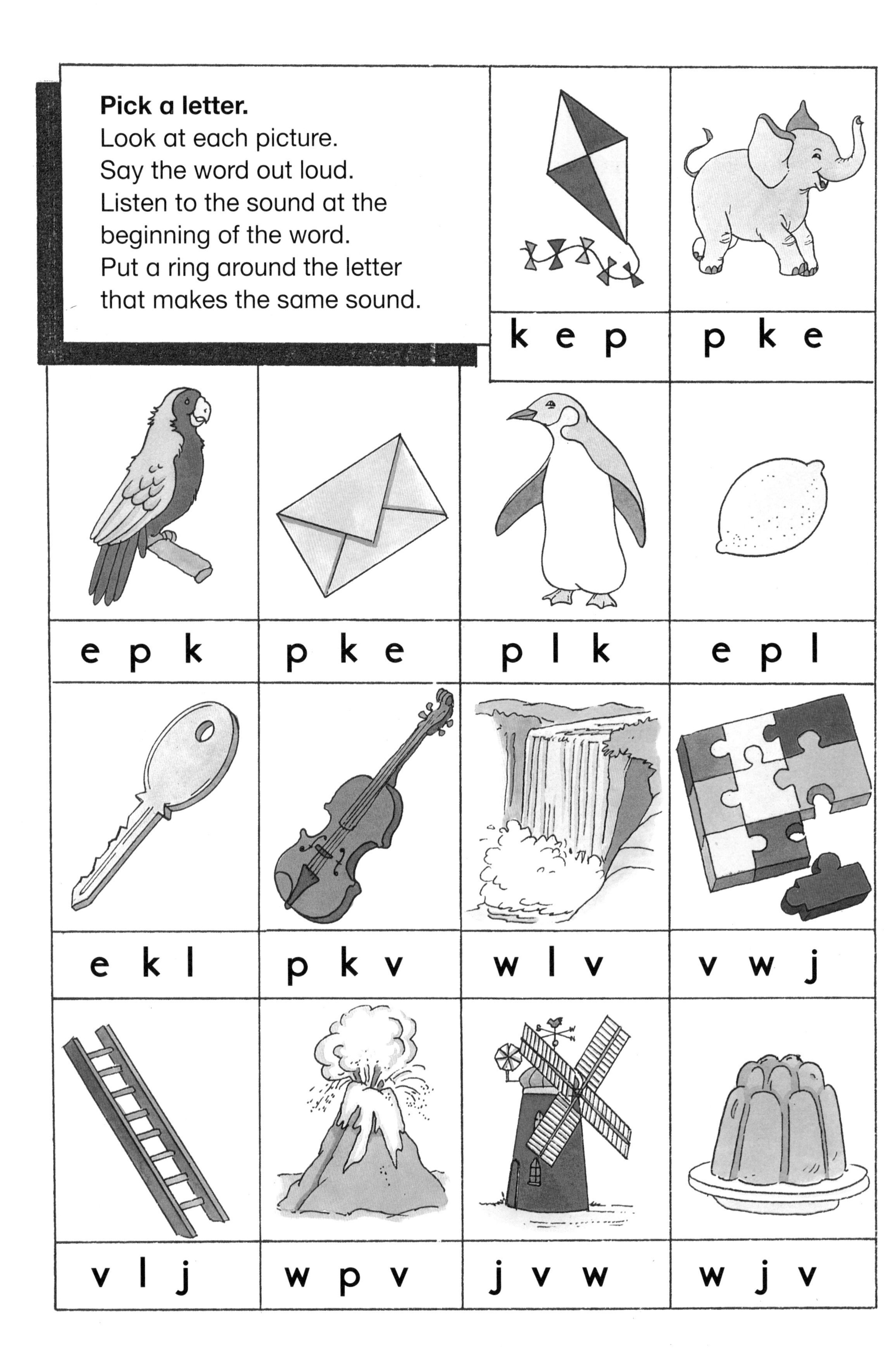

Pick a letter.
Look at each picture.
Say the word out loud.
Listen to the sound at the beginning of the word.
Put a ring around the letter that makes the same sound.
k e p
p k e
e p k
p k e
p l k
e p l
e k l
p k v
w l v
v w j
v l j
w p v
j v w
w j v

Eddy Elephant has organised an Easter Egg Hunt. He has hidden **e**leven **e**ggs and **e**veryone is out looking! Can you find all the **e**ggs?

Now find 2 things beginning with each letter. **v w j l k p**
As you find them, write their letter at the bottom of the page.

All Aboard the Letterland Express

Hurry, hurry! The train is leaving the station. There's **Dippy Duck** closing the door and **Fireman Fred** waving the flag.
2 to 6 people can play. First of all, draw a train like this. →
Every time you land on a question, write the correct letter in your train and have another go. You could fill your train full of Letterland people! If you don't know the answer, wait until your next go. Move forward the same number of squares as there are dots on the dice. Away we go!

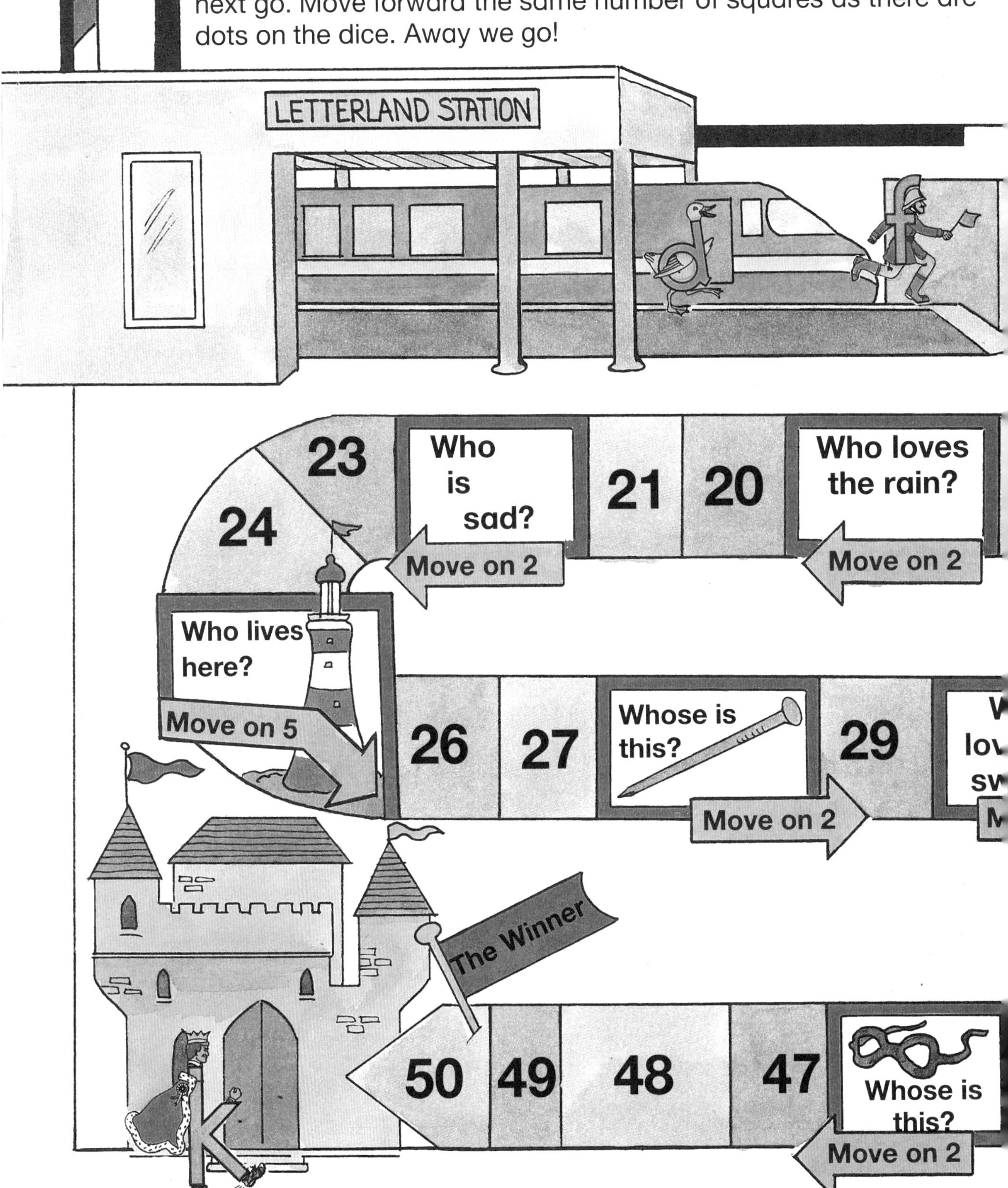

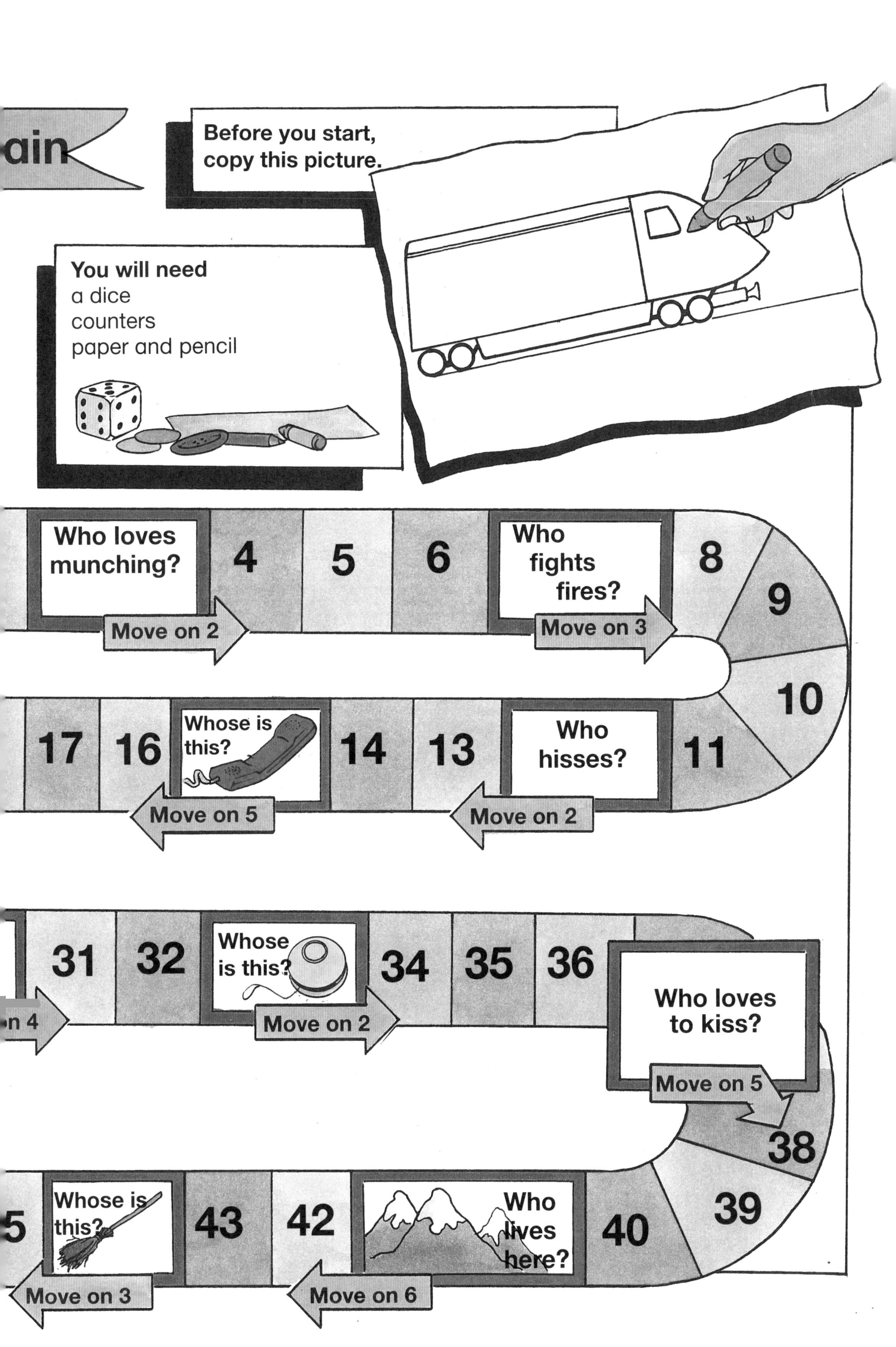
ain
Before you start, copy this picture.
You will need
a dice
counters
paper and pencil
Who loves munching?
Move on 2
4
5
6
Who fights fires?
Move on 3
8
9
10
11
Who hisses?
Move on 2
13
14
Whose is this?
Move on 5
16
17
31
32
Whose is this?
Move on 2
34
35
36
Who loves to kiss?
Move on 5
38
39
40
Who lives here?
Move on 6
42
43
Whose is this?
Move on 3
5

Find the missing letter.

Name the thing next to each word. Who can you hear starting that word?

It will be one of these Letterland friends.

Fill in their missing letter.

Who am I?

Fill in the letters to see which of these Letterland friends is missing from the words below.

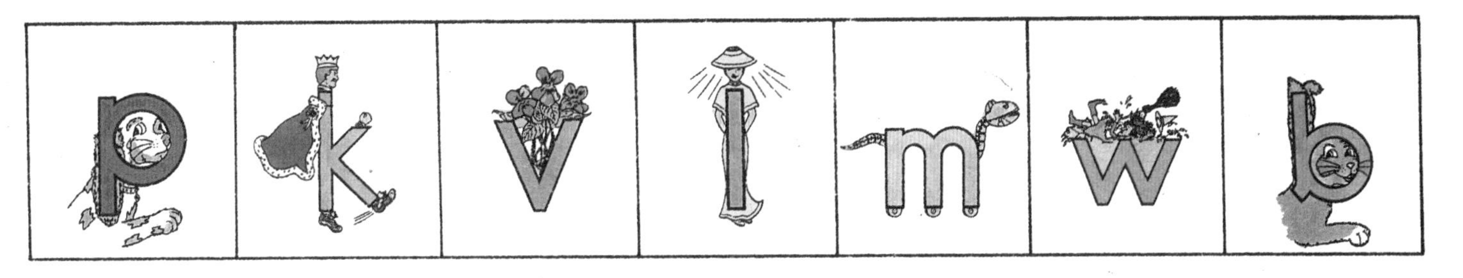

Write your answer here.

I love to kick. ________

I lo ve the light. ________

I love the wind. ________

I have petals. ________

Fireman Fred is having a Fancy Dress party.

Draw a line to match each person with their costume.
A small clue! Each person has chosen a costume that begins with the same sound as his or her name.)

I'm **Bouncy Ben**! I love to **b**ounce into words and make the sound at the start of my name. **B**ouncy **B**en.

Point and make my sound each time.

b b b b

Colour me in.

Let's make my letter. Start at the top of my ear, go down and up a little. Then go around my face.

Make my sound as you write.

Bouncy Ben's Bread

Put all the ingredients in a pan. Stir gently over a low heat until the dough begins to come away from the sides of the pan. Leave to cool, then knead for a few minutes until soft and springy. Use to make ornaments or jewellery. Bake in a very low oven for 2 hours and then leave in the oven to dry out completely.

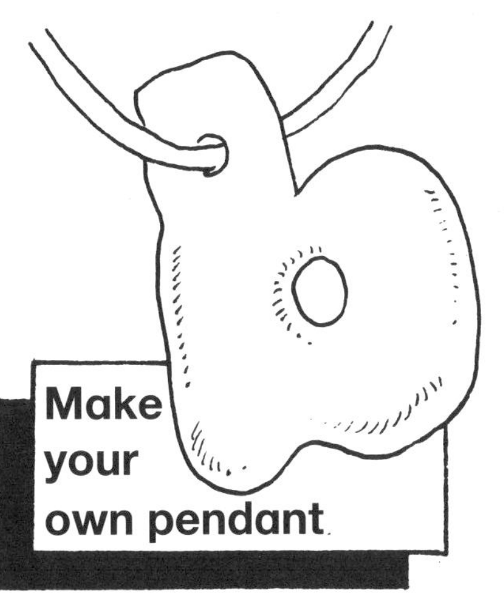

Make your own pendant

Make your own ornaments

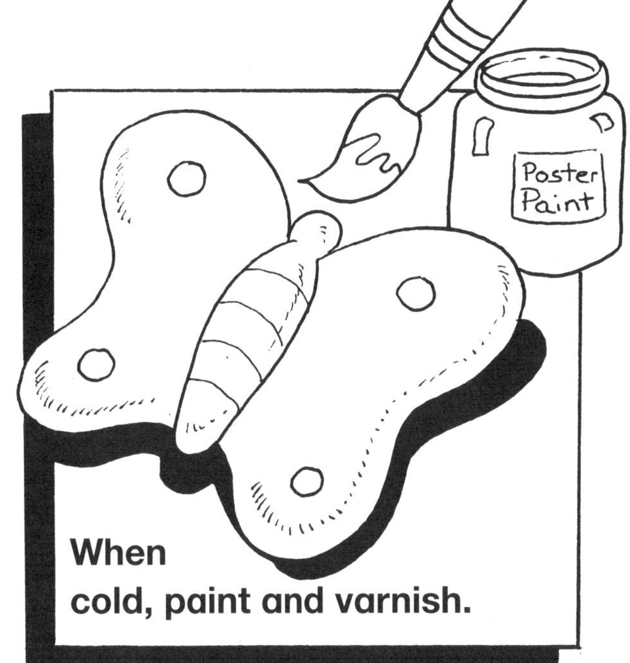

When cold, paint and varnish.

Look out everybody – here comes **Robber Red**!
In words he makes the growling sound at the beginning of his name. **R**obber **R**ed.

Point and make his sound each time.

r r r r

Colour him in.

To write his letter, start at his shoulder. Go down his body, then up and over to make his arm.

Make his sound as you write.

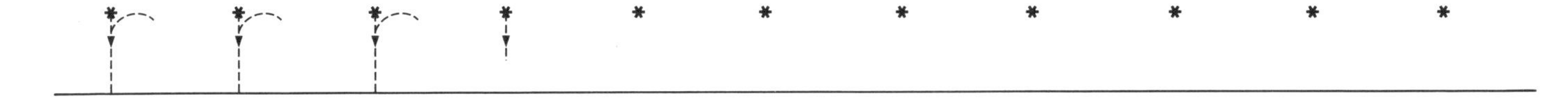

Watch out! **Robber Red** is about! What will he take? Draw a **r**ing around the things he will **r**ob. Remember, he only **r**obs things that begin with his growling sound, **r**.

Look at me **u**p high in the sky. I'm **Uppy Umbrella**! I make the sound at the start of my name. **U**ppy **U**mbrella.

Point and make my sound each time.

u u u u

Colour me in.

To make my letter, start on the side by my handle. Go down, round and **u**p – then straight down again.

Make my sound as you write.

I love the wind! It carries me **u**p high! But sometimes it blows my umbrella inside out and **u**pside down. Then I get very **u**pset!

It's a blustery day in Letterland.
Can you spot two inside-out **u**mbrellas?
Write my letter **u** **u**nder each **u**mbrella in the picture.

Hello! I'm **Quarrelsome Queen**. I don't **q**uarrel all the time. I can be **q**uiet, too. I make the **q**uick sound at the start of my name.
Quarrelsome **Q**ueen.

Point and make my sound each time.

q q q q

Colour me in.

To write my letter go all around my face and up to the top. Then down my hair with a **q**uick flick up at the bottom.

Make my sound softly as you write.

Quarrelsome Queen's jewels are **q**uite beautiful.

Here are **Max and Maxine**, the Kissing Cousins. They have a special sign which looks like two crossed lines. It stands for a kiss. If you say the word "kiss" in a whisper you will have their letter sound.

Colour in their sign.

To write their letter, draw two sticks crossing each other.

Whisper their sound as you write.

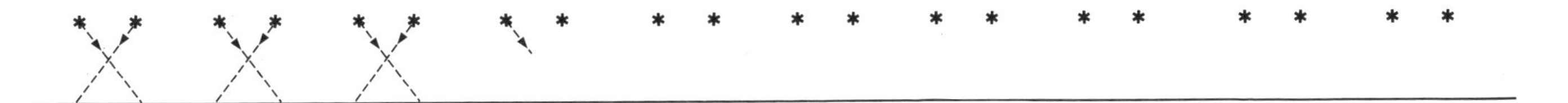

Look at each picture and say the word out loud. Listen to the sound at the beginning of the word. Put a ring around the letter that makes the same sound.

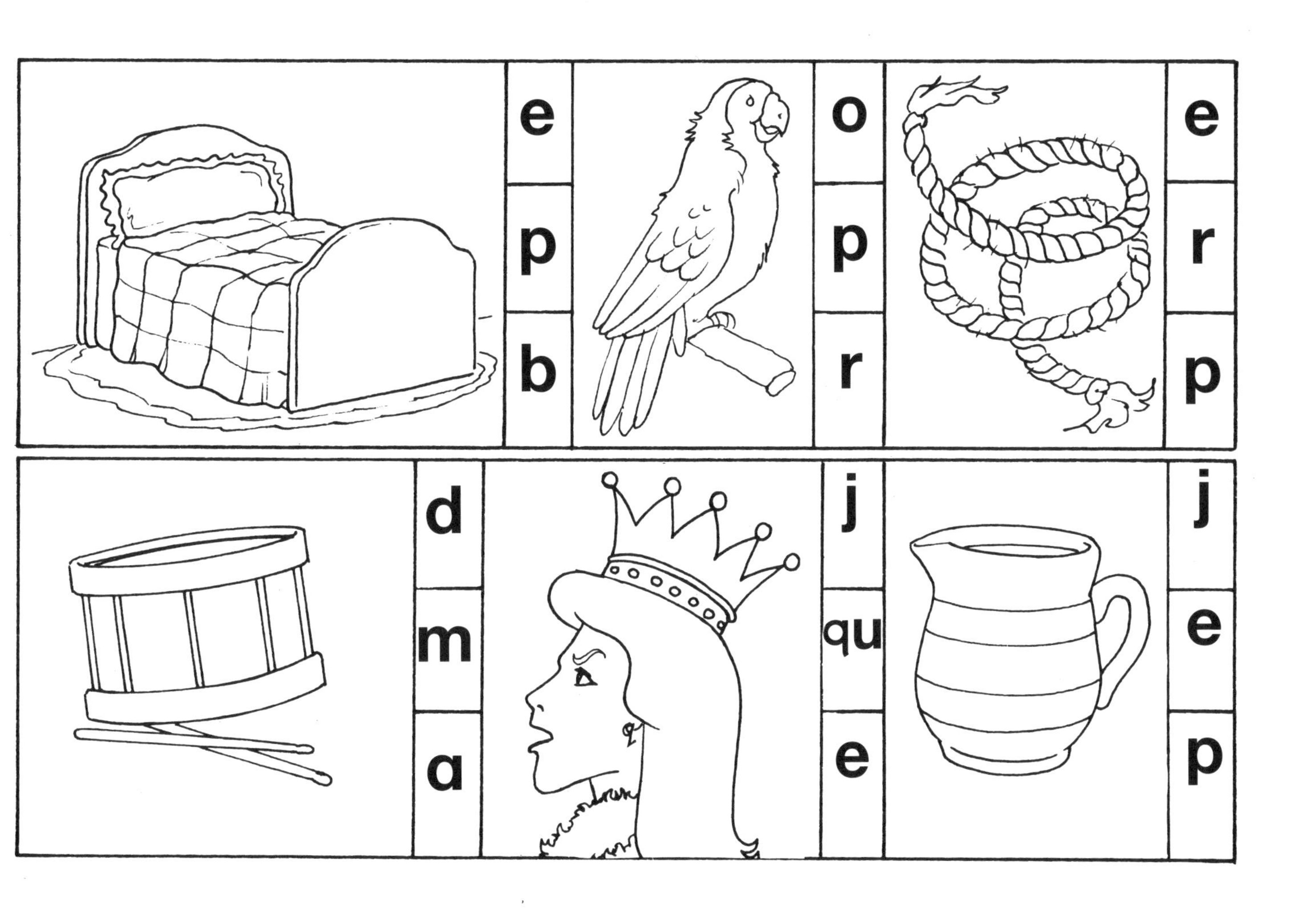

Hello. I am **Zig Zag Zebra**. I am very shy, but, if you like, I will tell you the sound I make in words. I make the sound at the start of my name.
Zig **Z**ag **Z**ebra.

Point and make my sound each time.

z z z z

Colour me in.

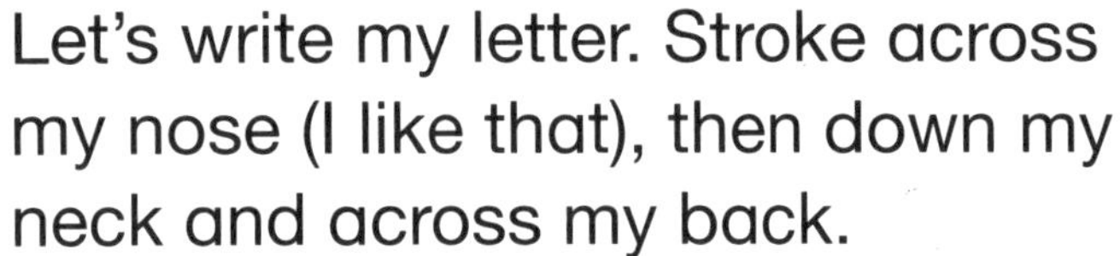

Let's write my letter. Stroke across my nose (I like that), then down my neck and across my back.

Make my sound as you write.

Can you draw a line and match each Letterland person or animal with his letter? Then copy the letter in the box.

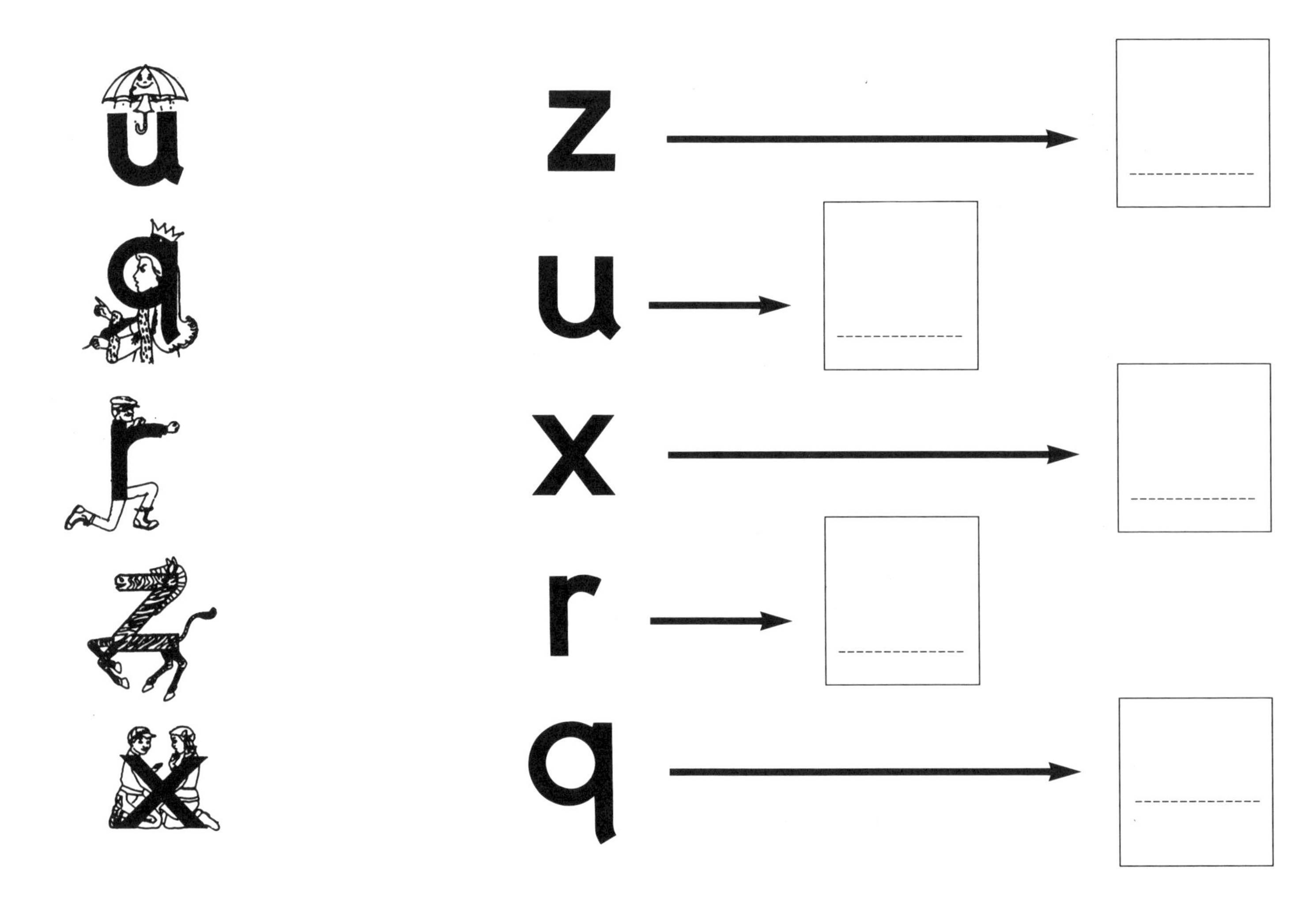

Some letters are missing.
Name the thing next to each word.
Who can you hear starting that word?
It will be one of these Letterland friends.
Fill in their missing letter.

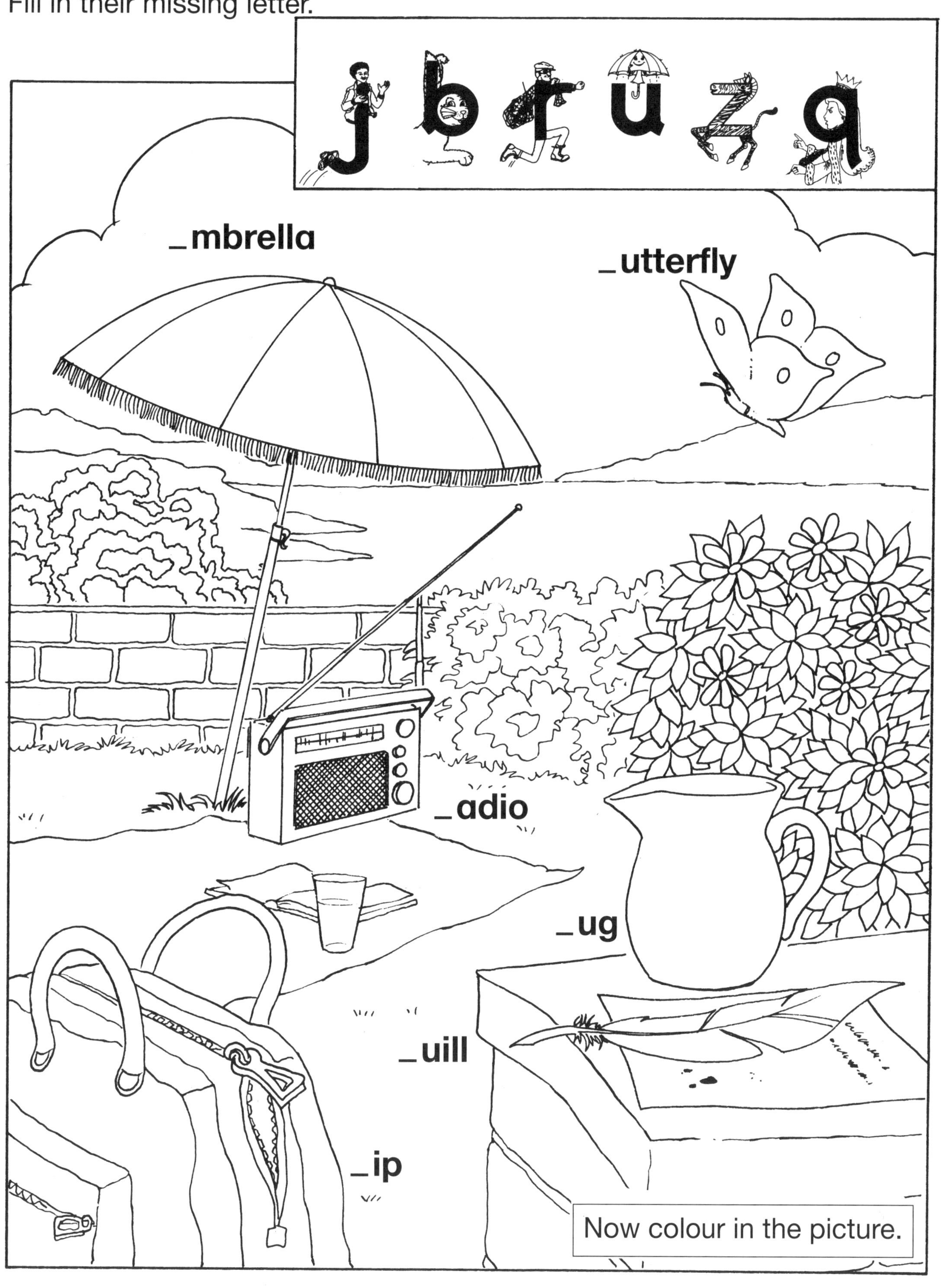

Impy Ink has drawn an invisible picture. Follow the letters of the alphabet, joining up the dots with your pencil. You should follow this order:

a b c d e f g h i j k l m n o p q r s t u v w x y z

Start at **Annie Apple's** letter and then go on to **Bouncy Ben's** letter. Who is after that? Yes – **Clever Cat**!

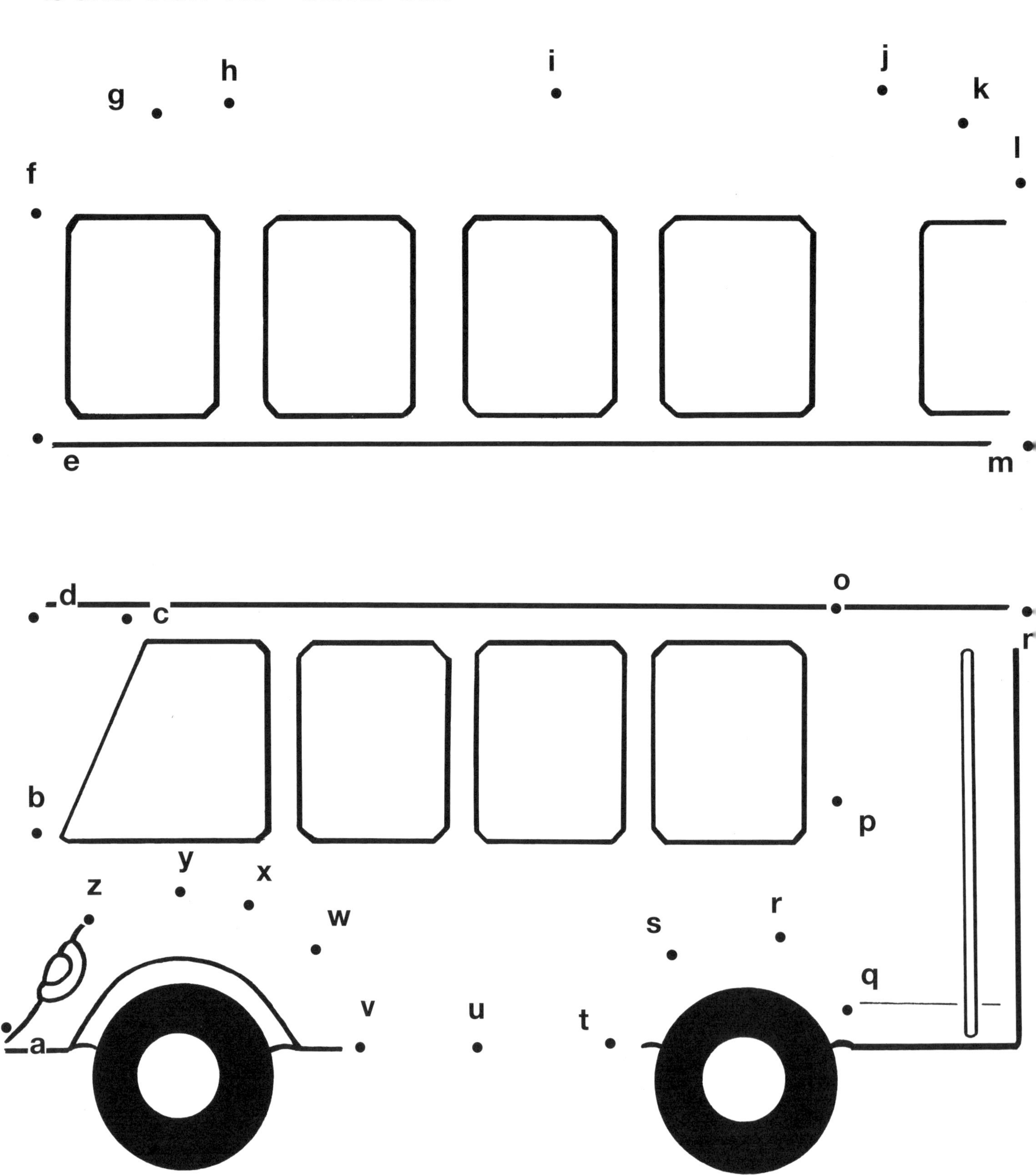